Changing the face

The Life and Times of Percy Dalton, City Engineer and Surveyor, 1926-1949

Researched and Compiled by
Marie K. Dickens

"The man who changed the face of Carlisle"
Carlisle Journal

HAYLOFT

First published 2002

Hayloft Publishing, Kirkby Stephen, Cumbria, CA17 4EU.
Tel. (017683) 42300 or fax. (017683) 41568
e-mail: dawn@hayloft.org.uk
Web: www.hayloft.org.uk

ISBN 0-9540711-9-0

A catalogue record for this book is available
from the British Library

Produced in Great Britain
Printed and bound in Hungary

Dedicated to the memory of Percy Dalton and all those who have made Carlisle the great City we know today.

ACKNOWLEDGMENTS

Firstly I would like to thank Miss Dorothy Dalton, daughter of Percy for her assistance and for the use of her private photographs, and Percy's grandson, Mr Angus Dalton and family.

I would also like to thank the staff of Cumbria Records Office, Carlisle Castle and the Carlisle Library for their help. Thanks also go to Cumberland Newspapers, Dalston Road for permission to reproduce photographs and reports, which originally appeared in the *Carlisle Journal* and *The Cumberland News*.

Every effort has been made to find and acknowledge the source of any other photographs used in this publication, however if I have missed anyone please accept my apologies.

CONTENTS

ILLUSTRATIONS

INTRODUCTION

I have briefly compiled the life and works of Percy Dalton as seen through the 'eyes' of the newspapers of the time, in the hope of giving some recognition to this modest man who "changed the face of Carlisle".

The Electric Lighting Station, James Street (Tullie House Museum)

The Power Station at Willow Holme, built in 1925, extended 1940 and 1942. (Cumbria County Library)

MR PERCY DALTON'S CAREER.

Percy Dalton was born to Margaret (nee Taylor) and Samuel Dalton, a book keeper on 21 January 1884 at Walton, Lancashire.

He received his schooling at Southport, first at Atherton House Preparatory School and afterwards at Searsbrick Street College. He was articled to Mr Gilbert Wilson C.E., of Southport, with whom he received valuable training on civil engineering and architectural works of different kinds. During his studies, Mr Dalton obtained diplomas in building, construction (honours stage), mathematics, solid geometry (South Kensington), brick work and carpentry and joinery (City & Guilds), gaining two scholarships, and also passed preliminary and intermediate examinations of the Royal Institute of British Architects.

After completing his articles he gained further experience as an assistant with the late Walter Webb, architect and surveyor for Whitehaven, and subsequently with Mr. Robert Beswick, MSA of Swindon and Messrs. A. & W. Scott Deakin, FRIBA of Shrewsbury. He was by examination an Associate Member of the Institution of Civil Engineers, (1910), an Associate of the Royal Institute of British Architects, and was awarded the Testamur of the Institution of Municipal and County Engineers (1918).

Percy Dalton first entered the service of the Carlisle Corporation in February 1909 as architectural and general assistant to Mr H. C. Marks, Esq., MICE, city engineer and surveyor. In May 1919, he was promoted to be deputy city surveyor and water engineer. When Mr Marks died in 1926, Mr Dalton was appointed to succeed him as city surveyor and water engineer.

Many works, both of engineering and architectural

CARLISLE CORPORATION
ELECTRICITY WORKS.
OPENED 26 MAY. 1927.
MEMBERS OF COMMITTEE.
ALDERMAN A.CREIGHTON. (MAYOR).
ALDERMAN R. DALTON, J.P. (CHAIRMAN). COUNCILLOR F. W. TASSELL. (DEPUTY-CHAIRMAN).
COUNCILLOR W. H. CANT. COUNCILLOR J. W. NICHOLSON.
" B.CARR. J.P. " J.R. POTTS.
" T. G. CHARLTON. " M. THOMPSON.
" MISS E. L. MUSGRAVE. " A. J. WATT.
OFFICIALS. " J.G. DALTON.
A. H. COLLINGWOOD. TOWN CLERK.
C. W. SALT. M. INST. E.E. CITY ELECTRICAL ENGINEER.
H.C. MARKS. M. INST. C.E.. ⎫ CITY ENGINEERS.
P. DALTON, A.M. INST. C.E. A.R.I.B.A.. ⎭

*Plaque to commemorate the opening of the Electricity works at Willow Holme,
(Dorothy Dalton)*

character, were designed and carried out by Mr Dalton. He will perhaps be best remembered for his housing schemes, he was put in charge of the city's housing programme early in 1919 and personally supervised it until his retirement. He never let any other scheme, however important interfere with housing progress. The result being "the face of the city has been changed," for under his supervision 22 new housing estates were built, including Longsowerby, (here Percy Road derived from Bishop Percy due to the fact the land was previously owned by the Dean & Chapter), Raffles (here Dalton Avenue) and Botcherby. Special designs for old people's dwellings were also included, such as Margaret Creighton Gardens.

Next in the public eye would perhaps be the five bridges which he designed carrying as they do the main traffic routes into the city. The first of which were the Caldew and the St. Nicholas; bridges which came under reconstruction whilst Mr Dalton was deputy to Mr Marks, were the Eden Bridge, the Warwick Road and the London Road.

Mr Dalton's first job when he came to Carlisle was to complete the erection of the Turkish Baths, which still stand on James Street. He was next to extend the electricity works on the other side of James Street, this he did in 1910 and he added another extension in 1913 (now the Carlisle Business & Enterprise Centre). Such was the rapid advance in the use of electricity, that in 1924 the corporation decided to build a new electricity power station at Willow Holme.

Mr Dalton designed and supervised the construction of the railway sidings and all the buildings of the new station, which was formally opened in 1927.

IFIED COPY OF AN ENTRY OF BIRTH

GIVEN AT THE GENERAL REGISTER OFFICE

Application Number _PAS A 112144 /97_

REGISTRATION DISTRICT				_West Derby_					
BIRTH in the Sub-district of _Walton_					in the _County of Lancaster_				
1	2	3	4	5	6	7	8	9	10
When and where born	Name, if any	Sex	Name and surname of father	Name, surname and maiden surname of mother	Occupation of father	Signature, description and residence of informant	When registered	Signature of registrar	Name entered after registration
4th ... ... Bury ... ... Road	_Bury_	_Boy_	_Samuel Dalton_	_Margaret Dalton formerly Taylor_	_Dock Keeper_	_S Dalton Father 9 Carisbrooke Road Walton_	_Thirtieth January 1881_	_Edwin Smith Registrar_	

IFIED to be a true copy of an entry in the certified copy of a Register of Births in the District above mentioned.

the GENERAL REGISTER OFFICE, under the Seal of the said Office, the _8th_ day of _July_ 19 _97_

*See note overleaf

This 1923 view, looking towards Scotland Road, shows the island block of property, including the Bird-in-Hand Inn, standing on the left. It was demolished in 1924 for road widening. The houses on the right of Church Street were demolished in 1931 to clear the approach to the reconstructed Eden Bridge. (Carlisle Archive series)

Carlisle Corporation were amongst the first authorities to support the establishment of community centres, and Mr Dalton made a special study of their design. His work in this connection was recognised by the National Council of Social Service.

As highway surveyor, Percy Dalton saw a transformation take place in the city's streets. In 1909 there were no asphalt nor tar macadam roads, only highways covered with cobble paving, whinstone cubes, whinstone chips and water-bound macadam. The latter were terribly dusty. In the summer a fleet of water carts patrolled the city to dampen the surfaces thus minimising the dust. The main roads into the city were all widened and reconstructed in tarred macadam or asphalt, along with the main streets within the city.

Many people complained of the bottle-neck near the Bird-In-Hand Inn at Stanwix, and were grateful for the improvement made there when the island block of property was demolished near Stanwix Church. The demolition of the Gaol (today Woolworth's) and the removal of the island block of property containing the Inn known as The Gaol Tap also improved another bottle-neck within the city.

The demolition of old property in Rickergate was in progress when war broke out in 1939. Mr Dalton was at that time engaged in making preliminary sketches of a design for new municipal buildings, and a large civic hall with accommodation for all kinds of civic functions, dances, concerts,

Mr. Percy Dalton at work in the Surveyors Office at No. 18 Fisher Street, now the Fisher Street Galleries. (Dorothy Dalton)

To commemorate the occasion of the 1928 Carlisle Pageant,
organised by Mr. Dalton. (Cumbria County Library)

conferences, with ample facilities for catering. Embodied in the scheme was a car park for patrons attending the functions.

Mr Dalton was responsible for the maintenance of all public parks and open spaces, and he personally designed the layout of Pleasureland (Hammonds Pond) and of Heysham Park (Raffles). He also carried out the garden design at the Stanwix end of the Eden Bridge, the plan of which was prepared by Mr Prentice Mawson. This garden was formed of old materials obtained from the Old Gaol, the old Eden Bridge and other sources.

A scheme for the creation of a physical culture centre on the Sauceries (Bitts Park) was approved for Government grant in 1939. This included levelling about 40 acres of playing fields and the building of a large swimming pool, two gymnasia and a public cafe. The levelling of playing fields in other parts of the city were also included in the scheme. The approvals and grants were withdrawn on the outbreak of war.

As water engineer, Mr Dalton duplicated the supply mains from Castle Carrock to Carlisle and also increased the filtering capacity at the works, thus augmenting the capacity of the works, which enabled them to meet the heavy strain placed upon them during the war years when daily consumption was very much greater than the maximum for which the works were originally designed.

Mr Dalton was also responsible for the widening and deepening of the River Petteril behind the houses on Greystone Road, to alleviate the problem of flooding (1928) at which time he provided a great service for the city with one of the first schemes in setting the many unemployed men back to work on the project. (The course of the River Petteril being diverted away from the backs of the houses in 1960s).

For the Health and Social Welfare Committees, schemes were carried out for the extension of The Infectious Diseases

Hospital, for the formation of the George Street scheme comprising maternity home, school clinic and tuberculosis dispensary (today Georgian Way); also extensive alterations were carried out at Fusehill and City General Hospital, (formerly Fusehill Workhouse, today St.Martins College).

For the Education Committee, Mr Dalton designed the open air school at Newtown and the senior schools at Currock. The latter scheme was approved by the Ministry of Education, and all plans were prepared by September 1939, when the scheme had to be deferred due to war. (One of the first things Mr Dalton did when he came to Carlisle was to make detailed reference plans of all the city schools, which plans proved invaluable in connection with the maintenance of over 20 schools). His last work of magnitude for the Education Committee was the preparation of key plans for all the city schools, both primary and secondary, showing how they could be altered and improved to fit in with a new development plan which had to be submitted to the Ministry of Education.

Much of Mr Dalton's works are buried underground. As the city became built up with the new houses, many miles of new housing roads had to be constructed and under these roads are buried many more miles of sewers, water mains and other services. Large and expensive relief sewers had to be constructed to carry sewerage from the new suburbs to the sewage disposal works. These engineering schemes cost hundreds of thousands of pounds, and include sewers of many sizes, some built in rock and in tunnel and some actually laid in the bed of the River Caldew. However in the carrying out of such schemes Percy Dalton saved Carlisle a matter of £17,000.

As town planning officer, Mr Dalton sometimes lectured on his town planning proposals. He used to say one of the greatest disappointments of his life was that the schemes which he had planned to carry out in the last ten years of service were all shattered by the war. In his opinion, the set back was bound to extend beyond the actual lost war years and there would be much lee-way to be made up. Mr Dalton was also of the opinion that Carlisle occupies a unique geographical position as a conference centre, but at that time it could not cater for any of the larger conferences because of the lack of a suitable conference hall and of sufficient hotel accommodation. If the civic hall scheme could be proceeded with in

MR. PERCY DALTON

Carlisle Holiday Week
Originator and Chief Organiser of the
Programme of Events
June 27th. to July 4th

This cartoon appeared in the Carlisle Journal, 30 June 1942. Dorothy Dalton recalls her father found it amusing.

Rickergate and the state management persuaded to build further accommodation, he believed that not only would Carlisle become a conference centre, but a popular tourist centre conveniently situated for touring the Roman wall, the Lakes and southern Scotland.

One of the last schemes to be carried out by Mr Dalton during his service was the erection of the police and fire buildings in Rickergate, which also included the police court and which was completed during the war.

Of matters outside his official duties which stood out in Mr Dalton's memories were the Carlisle Pageant in which he had much to do in preparing the Pageant arena and scenery; between the wars; the Civil Defence Organisation in which he was the chief officer in charge of the rescue, decontamination and repair services; and the stay-at-home holiday weeks which he organised in the summers of 1942, 1943, 1944 and 1945. Mr Dalton and his family also had a long association with Charlotte Street Congregational Church where he served as deacon for many years until ill health prevented him from attending regularly.

MEMORIES OF DOROTHY DALTON

Dorothy recalls: "It was through my fathers involvement in the running of the Sunday School at the Charlotte Street Congregational Church that he met my mother, Betty. My mother, Betty Robinson, was born in Carlisle and was private secretary to Mr Carr of Carr's Biscuit Factory in Caldewgate. She played the piano at the Sunday School."

Percy and Betty married in Spring 1916, and began married life living at Thornton Road, Stanwix. The following spring their first child was born, William Eric, known as Eric. Their second son, Kenneth Raymond, known as Ray was born in

Percy and Betty married in spring 1916, and began married life living at Thornton Road, Stanwix. The following spring, their first child was born, William Eric, known as Eric. Their second child, Kenneth Raymond, known as Ray was born in the spring of 1920.

On these pages various pictures of life at Eden Dene from Dorothy Dalton's collection

The opening of the new pavillion for Carlisle Golf Club, which stood at the entrance to Rosehill in 1911. (Ashley Kendall)

the spring of 1920. In 1927 the family moved to a larger house at No.26 Brampton Road named Eden Dene. This house along with No. 28 were designed and built by Mr Dalton. It was at Eden Dene where Dorothy was born, followed by John. Dorothy recalls: "Eden Dene was a family home, the garden was lawned with terraces reaching down to Rickerby Park.

"We were a real family, doing lots of things together. We would always have a proper sit down family Sunday dinner every week. Father had a billiard table and table tennis table at Eden Dene. He would organise family competitions which were great fun."

In his younger days Mr Dalton was very keen on cricket and tennis, and for many years was a member of the West End Bowling Club, which was situated on Goschen Road, off Dalston Road. Later he took up golf and for many years was a member of the Carlisle City Golf Club, which was then situated at Rose Hill, before moving to Aglionby, at which time the land was taken over as an Army Camp. Today it is Rose Hill Industrial Estate. Betty would also play golf with Percy. Today Dorothy is a member of Carlisle Golf Club and regularly plays in competitions. Dorothy recalls her father was also a member of the Non Alcoholic Border City Lodge, he did not drink himself, but was not against others having a tipple.

She said: "Father had a great love for the Lake District, to where we would regularly travel for family walks, picnics and holidays. Here my father would sketch and paint post card size watercolours of the scenery. Every year my father would have the month of August off work, we would all spend these holidays at Scarborough."

Mr Dalton was good friends with John William Laing of

This photograph was taken on a trip to the Lake District in Percy Dalton's first car. (Dorothy Dalton)

Lake District scenes taken from the pages fo Mr. Dalton's sketch book

John Laing & Son, builders, who were contracted by the council to carry out much of the housing scheme building in Carlisle. Dorothy has in her possession a book which was given to her father by John W Laing, in which is written:-

"A great deal of building was being done in the city. The Borough Surveyor for 40 years, Percy Dalton, found that he could trust John Laing & Son to do good work. He was opposed to the indiscriminate building of flats advocated by some other members of the Corporation, preferring separate houses as more appropriate in districts where there was ample space. In this and other matters Percy and John found themselves in agreement, and they were able to work on the basis of real friendship...."[1]

Dorothy fondly remembers the impact of her father's first time on a plane. She said: "It was on March 1st 1934. The plane, carrying my father and members of Carlisle Corporation left from the Carlisle and Municipal Airport, which was at that time situated at Kingstown.

Percy Dalton on Scarborough Beach.

This family photograph was taken while on holiday at Scarborough, prior to the birth of John. From left to right, Dorothy, Percy, Eric, Betty and Ray.

They flew to Belfast to attend a luncheon hosted by the Lord Mayor of Belfast. My father was amazed to see the City of Carlisle and his work from an aerial view."

Dorothy kept a scrap book containing the newspaper cuttings showing the people of Carlisle enjoying her father's stay-at-home holidays. Mr Dalton said: " I confess that the work entailed was enormous and engaged all of my spare time every year from February until the end of June when the events took place. The thanks I received from all sorts of people, many of whom I did not personally know, and the evident enjoyment of thousands of people of all ages was ample reward for anything I was able to do. One year I reckoned that I had a thousand volunteers on rota helping to run the events. The holiday weeks did not cost the rates a penny and there was actually a very small sum in hand at the end of the fourth year, which the committee disposed of."

Mr Dalton's eldest son was Eric, who married Joyce Studholme, the youngest daughter of the Mayor of Carlisle.

Members of Carlisle Corporation with the Lord Mayor of Belfast, who entertained them to luncheon in the City Hall. The visitors came by air. On the Lord Mayor's right is the Mayor of Carlisle(Alderman J. R. Potts, JP), and on his left is Mr. Harold Carr, JP. Mr. Dalton is second from the left, standing at the back. (Northern Whig photograph)

A group of the qualifiers for prizes at the children's carnival on Bitts Park.

Fun and frolic at Carlisle's holiday week. Thousands of spectators thronged Bitts Park to enjoy the man attractions of Carlisle's Holiday Week, which has proved an even greater success than in previous years. The picture gives a bird's eye view of the huge amusement centre and children's corner, which are always particularly popular.

Pictured left to right, Percy, John, Eric and Ray.

They had two children, Caroline and Robert. Eric began as a quantity surveyor before becoming a director for Laing's builders, with whom he travelled a lot. When the head office moved to London, Eric, not wanting to settle in London started and ran the Laing's Bristol offices.

The next son was Ray who was a captain in the army, serving in Egypt. On his return to Carlisle he joined Right, Brown & Strong's solicitors. Ray settled in Wetheral, marrying Margaret Dunlop, they had daughter named Gabriel and a son named Angus Mclure Dalton.

Angus Mclure ensured that the family name of Dalton continued in Carlisle with his own son named Angus John, who married Vikki. Angus and Vikki have a daughter named Iesha and a son, Angus James, who is in fact Mr Percy Dalton's great, great grandson.

John was the baby of the family and joined the RAF. After the war he worked for Cowans Sheldons & Co Ltd, crane makers of St.Nicholas. John then moved to the north east with the business when it was taken over by the Northern

A family photograph, back row, left to right - Percy Dalton, Betty, Dorothy, Joyce, Eric, Ray and John. Front row - Gabriel (Ray's daughter) and Caroline (Eric's daughter)

Margaret and Ray

Percy and Betty with baby Angus at Eden Dene, 1954

Engineering Industries Group, which saw the closure of the St.Nicholas works in 1987.

Dorothy was Percy and Betty's third child, she became articled to her father before becoming an architect on her father's staff at the City Surveyors Office at 18 Fisher Street. She was the only woman on the staff. Dorothy recalls she enjoyed her work, especially when out on site. Having worked on the Morton

West Housing Scheme, the Carlisle crematorium and also being responsible for the Carlisle schools for a period of time

Above. left to right, Vikki Dalton, Angus James Dalton, Angus McLure Dalton, Iesha Dalton and Angus John Dalton.

Left, Dorothy, Percy and Betty in the Lake District.

she has contributed a lot to the city in her own right. After her retirement she was requested to join the Board of the Two Castle Housing Association and also works in the Carlisle Cathedral shop on Friday mornings.

Speaking from her home

on Brampton Road Dorothy recalls: "Eden Dene, being a large family home became too big when there was only myself and my parents left at home.

"We moved here just a few years prior to my father's death. Being in failing health he wanted to see my mother settled in a smaller, more manageable house. My mother loved this area she used to say that she did not want to live anywhere other than Brampton Road because she thought it was the nicest entrance road into the City. My mother enjoyed life here until she died at the grand age of 97-years-old."

MR HENRY CAPNER MARKS

City of Carlisle Surveyor and Water Engineer for 30 years.

Mr H. C. Marks, a native of Wakefield, was born on 31 July 1857. After having held local government posts in several Yorkshire and Lancashire Boroughs he came to Carlisle in 1896 as successor to Mr W. Howard Smith. The duties of water engineer were added to his post on the retirement of Mr Hepworth.

It was under his supervision that the old 'Glovers' Row island block of buildings were cleared away. The widening of Caldewgate, which proved to be one of the preliminary steps, resulted in the re-construction of Caldew Bridge. The work in connection with the St.Nicholas Bridge was of equal importance. (Mr Marks died before its completion and Mr Percy Dalton was appointed to the post).

Many new streets and building estates grew up, all the houses on the Warwick Road to the east of Broad Street and Waterworks Lane (now St Aidens Road) sprang up. The city's growth during his term of office having led up, first to the extension of the boundaries and later to its elevation to the status of County Borough. Mr Marks designed the city's sewage

Mr. H. C. Marks, City Surveyor of Carlisle, at his desk in his office. The photograph was taken before Mr. Marks retired after 30 years' service. (Carlisle Journal, 16/7/26)

Glovers Row immediately before demolition, looking along Castle Street towards the Green Market. The entrance to St. Cuthberts Lane is on the extreme left. (Carlisle in Camera)

disposal works at Willowholme. When the electric tramways came to Carlisle, Mr Marks planned out the original cable routes.

Outside his official duties Mr Marks was a Freemason. For many years he was church warden at St. Aidens Church. As a young man he had played rugby for the West Riding, later becoming an enthusiastic golfer, being a member of the Carlisle and Silloth golf club for 23 years, 16 years serving on the committee.

Mr. Marks retired due to ill health in September 1926 and died on the 8 November 1926 at his residence in Howard Place. There was a large gathering in St.Aidens Church for his funeral.

THE APPOINTMENT OF MR DALTON

It was when Mr Marks retired due to ill health in September 1926 that Mr Percy Dalton took over as City of Carlisle engineer and surveyor, however there were certain members of the council who had their doubts about Percy taking up the position.

"On Tuesday, September 1926 the City Council appointed Mr Percy Dalton, the deputy surveyor to the office of City surveyor, which had become vacant through the resignation for health reasons of Mr H. C. Marks...

"The Council in selecting Mr Percy Dalton to succeed Mr Marks have acted on the principal of promoting a member of their own staff who has already proved his professional competence by his work in the office..." Mr Dalton's appointment was criticised by four Labour members on the grounds that so important a post should have been thrown open to public competition...

"The reply from the Health Committee being.... Mr Percy Dalton's credentials are so strong that no useful purpose would have been served by advertising for other applications for the post.... Promotion by merit is a sound method, and as the members of the Health Committee, who are in the best position to judge were unanimously in favour of Mr Dalton's appointment a formal advertising of the position would have been a rather futile and farcical proceeding."[2]

THE WORKS OF MR PERCY DALTON

The Carlisle Housing Programme

Prior to the first World War Carlisle was considered to be one of the most compact towns of its size in England. The cessation of building operations during the period of hostilities was followed by a great shortage of living accommodation, and one of the first post war problems that the City Council tackled was that of housing.

A census of houses within the city was taken, and a programme was formulated so that a start could be made immediately the intentions of the government were made known.

On the passing of the Housing Acts of 1919, which were known as the Addison Scheme a committee was appointed and the programme was put into operation. Two areas of land belonging to the corporation at Denton Street and Boustead's Grassing were first utilised, later land belonging to The Dean and Chapter was acquired at Longsowerby. This was followed by two sites at Wigton Road and Blackhall being purchased. As the programme expanded additional sites at Raffles and Newtown were acquired. At that time materials

Longsowerby, Richardson Road, New three bedroom type houses. (Carlisle Journal)

March 1928 and work is in progress on the corporation housing estate at Botcherby. Land was acquired from a Mr. Casey for use as playing fields. The remainder of the land was used for the erection of dwelling houses. Building began in 1928, with additional housing being built into the early 1930s. (Carlisle Journal, 2/3/28)

Raffles, Shadygrove Road, c1937, took its name from the name of a farm on Newtown Road. (Carlisle Library)

Dalton Avenue, c 1937, built to designs by Mr. Percy Dalton. (Carlisle Library)

Brookside, Raffles, c. 1937. Brookside was demolished in 2001 after the housing was found to be in a dilapidated condition. (Carlisle Library)

Community Hall, Raffles, c 1937, The Hall was opened in August 1934.
(Carlisle Library)

Paddling Pool, Heysham Park, c. 1937. In 1870 a Dr. Heysham of Carlisle
died leaving £1000 for the provision of a public park. Land at Raffles was
purchased in 1925 to create a new estate of around 1500 houses to replace
housing being cleared from slum areas of the city. Part of the land was set
aside for recreational use.

were very difficult to obtain and prices were very high. Nevertheless the council succeeded in erecting 208 houses under the terms of the first assisted scheme. A revision of the Housing Acts of 1923, The Chamberlain Acts, afforded slightly better facilities to local bodies, and a larger subsidy enabled the council to build 350 houses.

In 1924 The Housing Act was again reconstructed (the

Buchannan Road, Currock, c. 1937. The trees in the distance at the top of Buchannan Road being the area of upperby Park, formerly the site of the brickworks. As a result of extraction of clay for the use of the works, the original small pond became a lake. It was known locally as "Hammonds Pond" due to the fact that the land was also occupied by Archie Hammond and Son, Nurserymen and Florists. Mr. Hammond saw the potential for the development of the area and put boats on the lake, laid out a dance floor, tennis courts, cafe, animal cages and bridges. He opened Pleasureland to the public in the early 1920s. In 1928 Mr. Hammond died. In 1931 the area was acquired by Carlisle Council at which time further development took place to designs and under the supervision of Mr. Percy Dalton. The surrounding fields were developed into the council housing estates of Currock and Upperby. (Carlisle Library)

Pleasureland proved a strong attraction and the boats were greatly in demand. (Carlisle Journal, 12 June 1925)

Getting ready for the holidays at Pleasureland. (Carlisle Journal, 3 April 1931)

Wheatly Scheme) and an increased subsidy granted, of which the Housing Committee took full advantage. By the end of September 1927 the number of houses erected was 776.

A further extension of the period of the subsidy to March 1929 gave the committee another opportunity of extending contracts and an additional 600 houses were provided for. The number of houses built included some small houses which were intended for the accommodation of the tenants from slum clearance areas.

The first of the special designs for old peoples' dwellings were built in 1932, these being Margaret Creighton Gardens. The whole of the architectural work, construction of roads and sewers etc. and supervision of labour was carried out by Mr Percy Dalton. By his retirement in 1949 around 14,000 council homes had been erected, some 7000 of which were Laing's houses.[3]

In 1870 a Dr Heysham of Carlisle died leaving £1000 for the provision of a public park. Land at Raffles was purchased in 1925 to create a new estate of around 1500 houses to replace housing being cleared from slum areas of the city. Part of the land was set aside for recreational use.

An advertisement in the Carlisle Journal, 26 June 1925

Children's carnival at Pleasureland. (Carlisle Journal, 26 June 1931)

Holiday time - children making the most of fine weather on the roundabout at Pleasureland. (Carlisle Journal, 24 July 1931)

Margaret Creighton Gardens opened with a civic ceremony on 11 November 1932 (Carlisle Journal, 11 November 1932)

Old Greystone.

Margaret Creighton Gardens stand on a three and a quarter acre site, formerly a row of cottages dating from the 1830s, known as "Old Greystone." These were the first affordable and suitable housing for the aged. The total cost per house being £195 8s 6d. The houses were let at 4s 6d per week. Mr. Percy Dalton said: "Interest in the scheme has been manifested by Corporations as far apart as Aberdeen and Wales." The gardens were named after Margaret Creighton, wife of twice Mayor Archibald Creighton. She did a lot of good work for the poor and aged people of the city. Margaret Creighton died in October 1932, before the new houses were completed only a month later. (Carlisle Journal, 13 June 1931)

Margaret Creighton

Margaret Creighton Gardens.

Margaret Creighton Gardens. (Jackson file, 1937, Carlisle Library)

History of Caldew Bridge

In 1685/6 all that could be seen towards Caldewgate were a few scattered farms, and the fields and meadows of the Caldew Valley. Travellers from the west crossed the Little Caldew by means of a narrow wooden bridge, and then over a stone bridge of three arches, the central arch being dry and forming an island. An incline led to the present railway level and people crossed over the English Dam just outside the Irish Gate, which ran through a culvert. This denoted how English Damside got it's name.

In 1705 Bishop Nicholson, who resided at Rose Castle, in his diary of 8 April said: "We went to Carlisle in the coach in the morning passing with great hazard over Caldew Bridge in great danger of falling." In 1740 the parishioners of St. Mary's and the several villages round about petitioned the

Carlisle from the west in the 18th century, the approach road from the west over Caldew. Little Caldew and Mill Dam are shown. (M. E. Nutter)

Caldew Bridge, taking the main road to the west out of Carlisle. A motor bus crosses the bridge prior to its widening in 1925. (2nd photographic collection, Old Carlisle, Jim Templeton)

magistrates to make an order for the re-building of the bridge.

In 1812 some further improvements were made according to a stone found in the present bridge (1925). On the other side of the stone appeared the name of Thomas Blamire, Mayor, 1820. In that year two new bridges were erected ; one bridge of three segmental arches over the Little Caldew for the purpose of opening up better communication to the west and Canal Basin. After 105 years these bridges were being re-constructed.

In 1873 to get into Caldewgate from the city it was necessary to go down the Irish Gate Brow and up a steep incline. The years 1876 and 1877 saw the development of the Citadel Station, the construction of the new main line for passenger traffic, the building of an addition to the bridge and the doing away of the Irish Gate Brow. In 1925 the bridge was again reconstructed. When the work was finished and the block of houses at the corner of the west walls removed, a wider entrance made to Devonshire Walk, the parapet of the north side made similar to the south, and entrances to Brewery Row, Milbourne Street and Shaddongate completed, Carlisle would be second place to none in the North of England so far as bridges was concerned.[4]

The Rebuilding of The Caldew and St. Nicholas Bridges

In March 1923 it was proposed to improve and widen the Caldew Bridge, a number of properties were to be acquired for demolition before the work could be undertaken. These included The Wagon and Horses Inn, some housing on Brewery Row and Milbourne Street. By April 1924 the concrete foundation for one of the piers was completed and the demolition of the Rickergate property was proceeding with 25 men at work on the project. June 1924 saw the masonry on the west abutment completed. July 1924 saw a strike in the building trade interfere with the work on the Caldew Bridge.[5]

In regard to St Nicholas Bridge, plans were submitted for

The rebuilding of Caldew Bridge. (Carlisle Journal, 4 June 1926)

The St. Nicholas Bridge was too narrow and, as part of an improvement scheme to widen all road bridges in the city, this was rebuilt between 1926 and 1928. This view from St. Nicholas Street, looking towards Currock, was taken before work began. Behind the boarding on the left was Cowans, Sheldon & Co., and on the right the entrance into builders' and slaters' yards at Old St. Nicholas. *(Archive Photograph Series, Dennis Perriam)*

Re-construction of St. Nicholas Bridge (Carlisle Journal, 4 March 1927)

Re-construction of St. Nicholas Bridge. (Carlisle Journal, 20 May 1927)

the widening of the approaches and ends of St Nicholas Bridge on 23 October 1923. An agreement with the London and North Eastern Railway Company to acquire land was completed. As soon as specifications were returned, tenders were invited and work would begin. By September it was resolved to accept the tender of Messrs Laing and Son Ltd for the sum of £56,941 for the work to be carried out on St. Nicholas bridge. Work commenced on the widening of the St Nicholas Bridge on 29 September 1924. The work being hampered by bad weather in January 1926 which saw the foundations becoming flooded.

On 17 April 1925 the *Carlisle Journal* reported bridge building delays: "It was a year last October (1924) since negotiations commenced with the railway Companies in regard to the draft agreements for the bridges (St. Nicholas and Caldew Bridges). It had been hoped that during the winter

The opening of St. Nicholas Bridge, the Mayor, Mr. Henderson, cutting the ribbon and declaring the bridge open. (Carlisle Journal, 16 March 1928)

The opening of St. Nicholas Bridge - Miss Ethel Clayton presenting the Mayoress with a bouquet. (Carlisle Journal, 16 March 1928)

the unemployed would have been engaged in the work. Winter had come and gone and still there were matters on the agreement not settled... It was deplorable to think that work on the Caldew Bridge was standing half finished... It was not until 17 July 1925[6] that the delays were overcome and an agreement arranged with the London Midland and Scottish Railway Company in regard to the widening of that section of the Caldew Bridge."

On Friday, 6 November 1925 the *Carlisle Journal* reported on the unveiling of an inscription tablet to commemorate the Caldew Bridge improvements: "To the mayor fell the honour of unveiling the tablet which would commemorate for all time a record of the proceedings...

"The inscription read:

Caldew Bridge.
Reconstruction and widening, 1925.
Mayor-Alderman Robert Burns, JP
Chairman of the Highways and Streets Committee
Councillor John Minns
Town Clerk - A H Collingwood
City Engineer - Henry Marks. A M Inst. CE
Deputy City Engineer - Percy Dalton. AM Inst.CE,
A.R.I.B.A.

The Mayor's Congratulations

"The mayor said: "As one who has been intimately connected with this part of the city all my life, I am very pleased to be present this afternoon to mark another step forward in the widening of Caldew Bridge, which when completed will effect such a wonderful improvement, both for the residents of the district and the citizens at large. With the increase in motor traffic and the greatly increasing numbers of visitors to the Lake District from all parts of the country, this bridge has assumed great importance in the last few years, and in my opinion the widening and improvement of the bridge will be one of the greatest the city has ever carried out... I heartily congratulate Mr Marks (the city surveyor) and his assistant, Mr Percy Dalton, the contractors and all engaged on this bridge on the excellence of their work, and am convinced that those who follow us will fully appreciate the great advantages resulting from the widening of the bridge."

Mr John Minns said the mayor and himself had only one

The opening of Caldew Bridge, unveiling of an inscriptiion tablet. (Carlisle Journal, 6 November 1925)

The Mayor and Corporation officials are accompanied by the sergeant-at-arms (carrying the city mace) and the sword bearer at the opening ceremony for the reconstructed Caldew Bridge in 1926. The bronze plaque seen here was unfortunately lost when the bridge was further widened in 1973-4. Percy Dalton is pictured first on the left. (Carlisle Journal, 6 November 1925)

object, in the words of the late James Creighton: "To try to leave our ancient city a little better than we found it."

Re-opening of Caldew Bridge

The new bridge has been erected at a cost of about £40,000, but the Ministry of Transport contributed a grant equal to about half the cost. The bridge has a total width from parapet to parapet of seventy feet. The roadway is fifty feet wide, and there is a ten feet wide footpath on each side. The new structure replaces the old bridge, the roadway of which was only 22 feet wide.

The river arches are of concrete faced with stone, taken from Corsehill Quarries, near Annan, and in the portion over the railway there are steel joists embedded in concrete. The roadway is composed of granite sets on a concrete foundation reinforced with steel rods, the footpaths at the sides of the bridge being of Shap granite and concrete flags. Electric lamps have been provided on the parapet piers...

...The bridge was decorated with flags and shrubs in honour of the occasion. Shortly before three o'clock the members of the corporation gathered at the east end of the bridge where a blue ribbon was suspended across. On duty at the west side of the bridge were police officers, who stood with crossed halberds to prevent anyone from passing over the bridge before the ribbon had been cut...

...The Mayor (Mr G. E. Edmondson) stepped forward to the ribbon and said: "I hope that this bridge will be used to the benefit of the traffic passing over it. The bridge has been in a dangerous state for many years past, but all that has now passed, and we have today a handsome bridge."

Carlisle and its Bridges

Mr Charlton (councillor) said: "In Carlisle we had three rivers, consequently the provision of bridges had always occupied a very prominent place in the policy of the City Council. The river Caldew divided the city into two distinct portions, and consequently the necessity for good means of communication over the Caldew was of the utmost importance. The great change which had taken place in road traffic had also rendered the widening of the bridge an urgent necessity, because the bridge also afforded a means of communication between the two parts of the county... The better the facilities for communication in a city the more they could add to the prosperity of the city and the convenience of the citizens (cheers).

Cleaning up after the Caldewgate floods.

Caldewgate Floods

The mayor said: "In addition to the present Caldew Bridge improvement they had had in recent years the Port road and Wigton Road bridges widened and Caldewgate itself widened and improved so that it was now a fine thoroughfare... He knew Caldewgate people had suffered from flood... they were taking steps to deal with it and hoped the people of Caldewgate would not be harassed by floods. He wished them all good health and happiness (cheers).

Beauty of Carlisle

Mr J. H. Minns (chairman of City Council Highways and Street Committee) in proposing a toast said: "There were few cities which would compare with Carlisle for beauty and cleanliness, and there were few cities with as many bridges as

The re-opening of Caldew Bridge (Carlisle Journal, 29 October 1926)

Carlisle. His only regret was that they had not present with them the late Mr Marks... Mr Marks was a gentleman in every sense of the word, a credit to his profession and a faithful honest servant of the Carlisle Corporation... The contractors on the bridge had done their work very well, and he wished to pay tribute to the work Mr Percy Dalton, the city surveyor, had carried through in connection with the bridge."

Mr Percy Dalton responded to the toast, he said he was proud to be associated with an improvement which had been hailed with such acclamation. His pleasure would have been greatly enhanced if Mr Marks had been able to be present. He had been closely associated with Mr Marks for nearly 18 years, and they had always managed to agree... He had been fortunate in all the people he had had to deal with.[7] Mr Marks who was unable to attend the opening ceremony due to ill health died the following month on 8 November 1926.

The Eden Bridge

We know that the Roman wall crosses the Eden within a few hundred yards of the Eden Bridge, and excavations indicate that the Vallum actually passed under its northern approach, so we may be sure that a means of crossing the river existed in those far off days.

During medieval times, the River Eden between Rickergate and Stanwix divided itself into two branches, which were crossed by two wooden structures, called Eden and Priestbeck bridges. Being in a state of decay, these were taken down in 1600, when two narrow stone bridges were erected instead. In 1812 we find that the government of the day considered that a new bridge should be constructed over the Eden and advanced £10,000 towards the cost.

The bridge was 400 yards and its breadth between parapets, twelve yards, having a flagged pavement on each side of the carriage way for pedestrians. All the stone was brought from Cove, near Gretna. It was erected from designs, and under the superintendence of Robert Smirke, Jnr., Esq., RA. It is recorded that the bridge of 1812 cost £70,000[8]

The Priest Beck bridge, approach by Eden Terrace. (John Landseer, Carlisle, Sydney Torwill, 1991).

Carlisle from the north in 1795. The east wall of the city is decaying. Stone bridges span the old and new channels of the Eden, the Priest Beck bridge being some sixty yards upstream from the present bridge. (Robert Carlyle)

This photograph of Eden Bridge, looking towards Stanwix, was taken when the Corporation proposed a widening scheme. (Carlisle Journal 14 October 1927)

A farmer bringing his cow and sheep to the cattle market, crossing Eden Bridge in 1906. (175 Years of Carlisle, Cumberland News)

View of Eden Bridge, showing the congestion at certain periods of the day. (Carlisle Journal, 21 January 1927)

This photograph of Hardwick Cricus in 1931 was taken for evidence in an inquest on a motor accident in which a child was killed, hence the lettering and crosses. On the left are the ornate railings of the Sands Cattle Market and round this corner is the entrance into Newmarket Road and Dukes Road. The building on the right with hoardings was later demolished to make way for the Civic Centre. (Carlisle Coucnil, Carlisle in Camera)

"No doubt Robert Smirke would feel he had made it wide enough."[9]

For many years the narrowness of the bridge had been an inconvenience and just after the First World War, Mr Marks the then city surveyor, had prepared two alternative plans for widening and improving it, but these plans were not carried out on account of the cost. By 1930, however it was apparent that further delay was impossible and Mr. Percy Dalton was asked to submit a report and plan for widening and improving the bridge.

When plans had first been contemplated, the intention had

The widening of Eden Bridge and Scotland Road. (Carlisle Journal, 16 October 1931)

been to widen the bridge on the western or downstream side because of Eden Terrace and other house property on the eastern side of Stanwix Bank. By 1930 the council had acquired the whole of this property, so Percy Dalton prepared two plans. His plan for widening on the east side did not involve the demolition of Eden Terrace, but it did mean the destruction of the existing sloping access to the terrace and the building of an alternative road to it.

There was no doubt that by widening on the eastern side a much better and safer approach to the bridge from the north would be obtained. After taking into account the state of the Eden Terrace property, it was decided to demolish it too, a further consideration being that a fine view of Greeny Bank would be opened out and a much finer entrance to Rickerby Park from the north side of the bridge would be possible. So

The widening of Eden Bridge and Scotland Road. (Carlisle Journal, 21 April 1931)

A flood at Eden Bridge wrecked machinery being used in the Eden Bridge widening scheme. (Carlisle Journal, 6 November 1931)

plans for widening on the east side were adopted and the contract for the work was secured by Messrs. Matthew Muir and Co. of Kilmarnock. The total cost of the scheme was to be £60,000.

Because of the national importance of the bridge on one of the main trunk roads to Scotland, the Ministry of Transport made a grant of 75% of the cost, provided that not less than 25% of the men employed were recruited from the depressed areas.[10]

Mr. Minns (chairman of the City Council Highways and Streets Committee) said he had had the honour of proposing the adoption of three of the largest schemes for the erection

Eden Terrace, 1930. These properties were demolished in 1931 to make way for the widening of Eden Bridge. Gardens were laid out on part of the site in 1933. (Carlisle Archive Series)

The buildings of Eden Terrace, looking towards Rickerby Park.

The River Eden, looking towards Eden Terrace and the Eden Bridge, circa 1906. (175 Years of Carlisle, Cumberland News)

Workmen busy on a window of a house in Eden Terrace which is being demolished as part of the Eden Bridge widening scheme. (Carlisle Journal, 31 October 1930)

Workmen demolishing the houses of Eden Terrace, making way for "Eden Side." (Carlisle Journal, 31 October 1930)

of bridges that had ever been known in the City of Carlisle. St Nicholas Bridge and Caldew Bridge would stand as monuments to them as a Highways and Streets Committee, to the surveyor and everyone who had been connected with these works... The committee wanted the contractors... to get onto this work as many men as they possibly could in order to have the bridge completed as quickly as possible and to bring some benefit to the unemployed of the city. Eden Bridge was the 'Gateway to Scotland' and many thousands of eyes wanted to see a record for bridge building established in the City of Carlisle...

November 1931 saw the work hampered by floods as we can see from the *Carlisle Journal* of the time.

Gateway to Scotland

The civic opening ceremony of the widened Eden Bridge was performed at 12.15 pm on 27 October 1932, when the Mayor, Mr. Matthew Thompson unveiled a bronze tablet.

The Mayor (Mr. Matthew Thompson) unveiling the tablet on the Bridge.
(Carlisle Journal, 28 October 1932)

Immediately after the ceremony the civic party proceeded to the County Hotel where a luncheon was held and speeches were delivered in honour of the occasion.

Mr J. R. Potts said: "We have today passed another milestone in the history of Carlisle... The bridge is a work of art and a display of craftsmanship which is I am quite sure an asset not only to the architecture and artistic side of the city but to the commercial side of it... They were happy that the design of the bridge, as put forward by Robert Smirke, Junior, so many years ago had not been interfered with in any way... It was the asphalt surface laid in Botchergate that induced the Corporation to provide Eden Bridge with a similar surface..."

Mr. Percy Dalton's speech: "The first thing I did was to search as many old records as I could lay my hands upon to discover what was known of the original structure. No plans could be found and very little information of a useful nature

Spectators at the Eden Bridge opening ceremony. (Carlisle Journal, 28 October 1932)

Workmen busy with the last arch on the new portion of the bridge. (Carlisle Journal)

discovered. I was particularly anxious to ascertain the nature of the foundations... I found two references; one declared the bridge was founded entirely upon rock, the other said it was constructed partly upon rock and partly upon wooden piles. I had recently come across rock in the river bed a little further upstream when carrying out another contract, and from calculations we might reasonably expect to find rock under the four piers in the centre of the river. We actually found rock within two or three inches of the levels we had calculated, so we now had no fear of the foundations.

"The question of stone to be used was another interesting problem. The original stone came from Cove Quarry, a few miles north of the Border. I went to visit this quarry. Enquiries in the district disclosed the fact there was such a quarry, but I should have had great difficulty in finding it had

CITY OF CARLISLE
EDEN BRIDGE IMPROVEMENT 1932
ALDERMAN MATTHEW THOMPSON, MAYOR
MEMBERS OF THE HIGHWAYS AND STREETS COMMITTEE.
COUNR JOHN R. POTTS, CHAIRMAN. ALDN T. C. CHARLTON, A.R.I.B.A., J.P., VICE CHAI
ALDN T. ROGERSON. COUNR C. W. HILL. COUNR L. NORTH.
COUNR J. G. DALTON. J. H. MINNS. J. C. STUDHOL
R. S. HARRISON. B. B. MURRAY. J. THOMLINSC
RED & G. WEBSTER, TOWN CLERK. PERCY DALTON, A.M.INST.C.E., A.R.I.B.A. CITY ENGIF
MATTHEW MUIR & CO. LTD. CONTRACTORS.

Mr. Matthew Thompson, Mayor of Carlisle, who reopened Eden Bridge, with Mr. Percy Dalton, city surveyor, who planned the widening and improvement of the bridge and its approaches, thus making what many travellers consider to be one of the finest entrances to any city. (Cumberland News, 11 October 1957)

not a charming village maiden offered to accompany me in my car to direct me. I found the quarry was filled with water and had not been worked for over 70 years... All the rock was red sandstone. I made further enquiry, and found that the white stone had come from the very bottom... at a tremendous depth under the water, and as far as was known all the white stone had been abstracted before the quarry was abandoned.

"I next embarked upon a search to find a stone which would match the Cove stone. I visited several quarries and ultimately found what I wanted at a little spot called Greenlaw in Northumberland... The stone was of excellent quality, and is extremely difficult to detect any difference now the bridge is built...The new half of the bridge is constructed entirely of concrete reinforced steel, being merely faced with stone to preserve the design. This is in accordance with modern practice and gives enormous strength.

"I have often been asked why I did not widen the entire bridge using stone to match the old part. There were several reasons for this. To begin with the cost would have been much greater... Another reason was that the top of the old stone arches were so close to the road surface that there was no room for water and gas mains without cutting into the arches. As much larger pipes are now necessary, it was decided to use a modern reinforced concrete construction, which permitted of a much thinner arch, thus providing room for the pipes to be placed over them.

"All the services have been laid under the foot ways, so that the carriageway will not need to be disturbed. The wide carriageway has been surfaced with asphalt by the Limmer & Trinidad Lake Asphalt Company."[11]

The New Entrance to Rickerby Park

The garden which forms an imposing entrance from Eden Bridge into Rickerby Park was opened on Thursday 21 December 1932, by the Mayor of Carlisle, Councillor E. B. Grey.

The construction of the gardens was the means of providing employment for a number of unemployed men of the city. The scheme being carried out for £3,450, the estimated cost was £5,000 but savings effected were due entirely to the use of old materials. The site of the gardens was formerly occupied by a terrace of old houses which were demolished in connection with the Eden Bridge improvement.

Behind the terrace of old houses known as Eden Terrace

Eden Terrace, Eden Bridge, Carlisle. (Carlisle Journal)

existed a high retaining wall, upholding part of Greeny Bank, which was richly wooded at that spot. This wall was used to form an effective background to the garden scheme.

A remarkable feature of the whole scheme was the economy which was effected by the use of old materials. For instance, the white stone forming the rest houses came from demolition of the old Eden Bridge parapets, whilst the stone slates came partly from the demolition of old property standing on the site now occupied by the Margaret Creighton Gardens, the remainder being taken from an old barn at Caldbeck.

The steps which flank the lily pond provide another example of the artistic use of old materials, being formed of broken paving flags. The same material was used in all the footpaths on the square terraces. The red sandstone used in the walls was taken from the old gaol in English Street.

The whole scheme was carried out by Mr. Percy Dalton, who prepared all the details from a sketch supplied by a Mr. Prentice Mawson of London and Lancaster.[12]

Botcherby Bridge, Warwick Road.

In 1931 the widening of the bridge over the River Petteril on Warwick Road was one of the schemes included in a five year programme of road improvements around the City of Carlisle, under the supervision of the surveyor, Mr. Percy Dalton.

The Botcherby Bridge was constructed by Messrs. Matthew Muir & Co. Ltd. at a cost of around £5,555 2s 10d.

Petteril Bridge, Warwick Road, Carlisle, before the widening scheme. (Carlisle Journal, 13 December 1929)

The widening of Petteril Bridge, showing the narrow margin left for vehicular traffic. (Carlisle Journal, 19 May 1931)

City road improvements - this pictures showsthe old and new road levels on the Warwick Road at Botcherby. (Carlisle Journal, 6 October 1931)

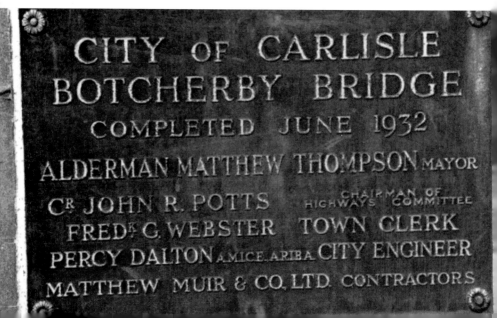

CITY OF CARLISLE
BOTCHERBY BRIDGE
COMPLETED JUNE 1932
ALDERMAN MATTHEW THOMPSON MAYOR
Cᴿ JOHN R. POTTS CHAIRMAN OF HIGHWAYS COMMITTEE
FREDᴷ G. WEBSTER TOWN CLERK
PERCY DALTON A.M.I.C.E. A.R.I.B.A CITY ENGINEER
MATTHEW MUIR & CO. LTD. CONTRACTORS

It was completed in June 1932. Matthew Muir & Co. were also the contractors for the Eden Bridge.

The London Road Bridge.

The bridge over the River Petteril on London Road has been referred to as the Petteril Bridge, the Harraby Bridge or the Mains Bridge. The latter because of its close proximity to the Mains Cotton Mill (today the site of Bendalls).

In April 1828 the bridge master reported the Harraby Bridge to be in a dangerous state, the water had worked its way at least six feet below the foundations. The following February the *Carlisle Journal* reported that the centre arch of this old and inconvenient structure, which was about to be pulled down had actually fallen down during the night of

The medieval bridge over the Petteril.

A photograph of the 1830 bridge, seen in 1897. (Carlisle in Camera)

Thursday, 26 February. No persons were harmed, railings were erected and a guard placed to prevent anyone from using the bridge. A temporary wooden bridge was erected until the new bridge was completed.

During excavations for the new road workmen discovered a lead coffin at Gallows Hill, a week later an oak coffin and an urn containing bones were unearthed.

In December 1832 the last stone in the arch work of the bridge was inserted with customary ceremonies. The parapets were erected the following spring. The bridge in those days had a flat low parapet which was a hazard - many a hat was lost and many an umbrella was blown inside out.

Changing the course of the Petteril. (Carlisle Journal, 5 August 1931)

In November 1938 the town clerk reported that the Ministry of Transport were to make a grant of 60% of the estimated cost of widening and improvement of London Road, including the widening of Harraby Bridge. Mr. Percy Dalton submitted five tenders for the work, with the tender of Mr. A. E. Farr of London being accepted at the sum of £12,989 11s 6d.

The River Petteril alterations behind Greystone Road

Percy Dalston's scheme for diverting the course of the River Petteril behind the houses of Greystone Road with a view to alleviating flooding and providing work for the relief of the unem-

A cold job - workmen clearing the bed of the Petteril. (Carlisle Journal, 5 August 1931)

ployment took place in 1931. At this time the river was widened and deepened.

Further work was carried out in the 1960s which saw the River Petteril diverted into the present channel away from the backs of the houses.

The demolition of the Gaol and widening of English Street.

The demolition of the gaol and the redevelopment of the site (today Woolworths) in conjunction with the widening out of English Street, necessitated the demolition of an island block of property which was the site of The Carlisle Arms, also known as The Gaol Tap due to the fact that it stood opposite the gates of the gaol and was the first stopping off point made by newly released prisoners. "This island block of property had caused a bottleneck, in fact over 50 years ago (1900)."[13]

The Carlisle Arms, also known as the "Gaol Tap", seen here in 1897. (Carlisle Archive Series)

Work has commenced to pull down the Gaol Wall. The site was sold for shops.
(Carlisle Journal, 29 April 1932)

The "wreck" of the Carlisle Arms - the public house was rapidly demolished in connection with the development of the "island" site. (Carlisle Journal, 25 November 1930)

A general view of "A" hall, showing cells capable of holding over 100 prisoners. (Carlisle Journal, 6 October 1925)

The demolition of Carlisle's old gaol. The building was demolished to make way for modern garages. (Carlisle Journal, 7 Februray 1936)

English Street island site, looking down on the site, showing the extra width gained at the Viaduct corner. (Carlisle Journal, 5 January 1932)

A striking photograh taken from the top floor of Natproban Chambers, on the Viaduct. The photograph shows the workmen engaged in demolishing the wall of the old Carlisle gaol. The site is to be used for business premises. (Carlisle Journal, 9 September 1932)

The rope and the black flag - these were used for the last time in 1922 for the execution of a man named Wilson. (Carlisle Journal, 6 October 1925)

Above, a glimpse through the prison gates where stones are being broken ready for street improvements. (Carlisle Journal, 9 February 1932)

Left, a corner of the execution shed - the scaffold has been demolished but the broken brick work marks the site. (Carlisle Journal, 6 October 1925)

The new road at the back of the old goal, looking towards the Viaduct.
(Carlisle Journal, 12 March 1929)

The old prison site - preparations for construction of the new street. *(Carlisle Journal, 2 November 1928)*

The above photographs show the entrance into English Street, showing the effect of the removal of the Lonsdale Monument and the construction of archways through the porches at the Court. (Carlisle Journal, 3 September 1929)

The Fire and Police Headquarters, Rickergate

This building was formerly the Assembly Rooms of 1887, later becoming the Star Music Hall. Eleven years later the Music Hall closed to become first a Salvation Army Citadel and later a band practice room. The property was demolished in 1938 to make way for the present day fire and police

A drawing of the new city fire and police station to be built in Rickergate. (Carlisle Journal, 11 December 1936)

headquarters in Rickergate, which was erected by Messrs. John Laing & Son Ltd., to plans designed by Mr. Percy Dalton (City Surveyor & Engineer, 1921-1949).

The station was built of stone from Greenlaw Quarry, Northumberland, and artificial stone to match. Attractive cottages for the permanent members of the brigade were provided in Warwick Street, which along with Peter Street was considerably widened. It may be of interest to note here that Greenlaw Quarry was also the source of stone used for Percy Dalton's scheme for the widening of the Eden Bridges in 1932.

Carlisle's new fire station when nearly completed. The photograph is taken from Peter Street. (Carlisle Journal, 17 February 1940)

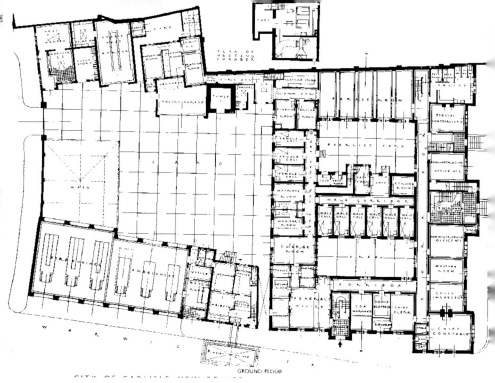

City of Carlisle new Police and Fire Brigade Headquarters.

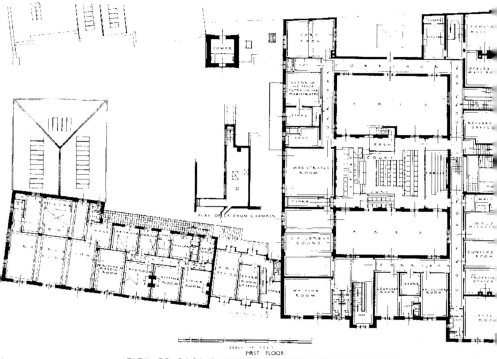

CITY OF CARLISLE NEW POLICE HEADQUARTERS

After forty years of tenancy of a building in Spring Gardens Lane, which had cost £521, the Carlisle Fire Brigade moved to their new station in Rickergate, which was erected at a cost of £26,968. The completed scheme, which would eventually include the Police Station, was estimated to cost around £63,000.

The opening ceremony of the new Fire headquarters took place on Thursday, 15 August 1940, and was attended by a large and representative gathering of members of the City Council, magistrates, officials and prominent citizens. Mr. F. W. Tassell, chairman of the Watch Committee received the

The Fire Station tower. (Official Architect, June 1941)

mayor and mayoress; he invited the former to open the new premises, describing the new station as: "the accomplishment of a long felt desire of the utmost importance." He then handed the key of the station to the mayor who unlocked the control room.

The *Carlisle Journal* reported that Mr. Dalton visited several of the newest fire stations whilst he was designing this station, and he confidently claimed that it contained the very latest equipment which was obtainable. The *Journal* then went on to give a full account of the proceedings.

Percy Dalton described his scheme as follows: "The Fire Station contains an engine room, which can accommodate six engines and adjoining this is the watch room, which was the nerve centre of the whole. Above on the next floor, was a large recreation room and adjoining this a reading room. A movable partition separates the two; when this is rolled back the reading room provides space for a stage and the recreational room becomes an auditorium for social occasions. There is also a billiards room upstairs, and the superintendents flat... To save time when the men have to take up their action stations a sliding pole connects the upper floor with the engine room...

"When the engines returned from a fire they come through a gate way into a parade yard. They are washed undercover... On the other side of the parade is a garage for police cars and a workshop for over hauling the fire engines, also there is a 97 feet high hose drying tower. There is a well equipped mortuary and post mortem room, a bicycle shed, dog kennels and a complete decontamination centre."

It should be pointed out that this scheme was designed long before war broke out. It was necessary to make certain variations in the plan and specification to meet war conditions.

The Mayor of Carlisle opened the door of Carlisle's new £29.000, all-electric fire station. The station was part of a large scheme which includes a new police station, court house and firemen's cottages. (Carlisle Journal, 17 August 1940)

This picture shows the progress on Carlisle city firemen's houses, part of the Rickergate development of a new police and fire station. (Carlisle Journal, 10 October 1939)

Referring again to the watch room, Mr. Dalton said: "It was intended to have a number of fire alarm pillars placed in every section of the city. From any one of these it will be possible to make an immediate call for the police or fire brigade... When the call reaches the man on duty in the watch room in front of him is a bright shining panel with all sorts of switches and knobs on it and behind the panel a maze of wires, cables and electrical gadgets of various kinds, which all go to make what he would like to call a mechanical brain... It had its limitations, however, he could not get a gadget arranged for pulling the firemen out of bed and putting on his clothes (laughter)."

(Official Architect, June 1941)

In conclusion Mr. Dalton said: "he would like to pay tribute to Messrs. Laing's and their sub-contractors for the splendid way in which they have carried out the work."

The mayor inspected the company of section officers; patrol officers and leading firemen of the city whom were on parade under Sergeant Rae, representative of the services' total strength of 259.

The mayor said: "We have reason to be profoundly thankful that the project was well under way before the outbreak of war. It is terrible to contemplate what might have happened had it been deferred, and they had been the victims of bombardment... We are very proud of you in Carlisle... At a time when everyone is doing some form of voluntary service, I cannot conceive of anything that is more important than the work you are doing to protect the life and property of the city."

Mr. J.W. Laing presented the mayor with a grandmother clock as a memento of the occasion. Mr. F. W. Tassell

Sessions Court, interior from the Bench (Official Architect, June 1941)

Main Buildings (Official Architect, June 1941)

The Mayor unlocking the door of the new city police headquarters in Rickergate. On his left is Mr. F. W. Tassell, chairman of the Watch Committee. (Carlisle Journal, 18 April 1941)

complimented Mr. Dalton upon the planning of the Station and said it was one more monument to his many successes.

On the opposite side of Warwick Street, nine self contained houses were built for firemen. These were designed in keeping with the main buildings.

The remainder of the buildings comprised of a completely modern police station containing about 100 separate rooms devoted to various purposes, including a large court house.

Situated between the police office and the fire station was a small separate block of buildings. The ground floor accommodated the Weights and Measures department. There was a small general office, the inspector's office and rooms for testing weights and measures. Outside the weights office was a large public weighbridge built in the carriageway, which could weigh vehicles up to 30 tons.

The police station was opened in April 1941 by the mayor. The *Carlisle Journal* reported: "A building worthy of the City... Mr. Tassell said the day marked another epoch in the history of their ancient City of Carlisle... The site cost £18,297, the buildings £63,000..."

The building was once more described as being amongst the many monuments which stand to Mr. Percy Dalton, who went on to describe his scheme.

END OF AN EPOCH IN THE HISTORY OF CARLISLE

The retirement this month of Mr. Percy Dalton, the City Engineer and Architect may be said to mark the end of an epoch in the City of Carlisle... In the many structural changes that have taken place, Mr Dalton's has been the guiding hand, wrote the *Carlisle Journal*.

But Mr Dalton always wanted something more. Many of his plans had to be shelved because of the war and among them were the designs for transforming the Sauceries into a great public recreation ground with open air swimming bath, games pitches and cafe. Another plan was the alterations to the markets to bring uniformity to the stalls and set apart a

John Walker, youngest member of the staff, presented gifts to Mr. Percy Dalton, retiring city engineer and surveyor, at a gathering in the Primrose Cafe. (Carlisle Journal)

concert hall. He has still more ambitious schemes, which include a Civic Centre and a great new highway from the west. These must wait for a more favourable day.[14]

Mr. Percy Dalton's 40 year services to the city, 21 years as surveyor were recognised by sincere tributes paid to him. Throughout these 40 years, said the mayor, Mr. Dalton has carried out on behalf of the corporation many works both of an engineering and architectural character... Mr. Dalton's work has been distinguished by efficiency and ingenuity. His vision and forethought have made the city what it is today... They would have to go a long way to find another official who could combine both duties.

Mr. Dalton replied: "I have always set myself a high standard. I have never been able to satisfy myself but it is nice to know I have given some satisfaction to other people. I have always enjoyed my work. I have been happy in it. If I have had any success, it is in the first place because I have tremendous pride in my profession, secondly, because I have great faith in my fellow men... and thirdly, because I feel that in carrying out public works and social services I was adding to the safety, convenience and enjoyment of thousands of my fellow citizens.[15]

On Thursday, 20 January 1949. past and present members of the staff of the Carlisle Corporation Surveyors' department gathered in the Primrose Cafe, Stanwix to pay tributes to Mr. Percy Dalton. He was presented with gifts and with an illuminated address by the staff of the corporation, referring to him as the "chief".

The *Cumberland News* went on to report: "Several of the works designed and carried out by Mr. Dalton are of particular importance and interest... the result being that 'the face of the city has been changed.'"

Mr. Dalton did not forget to thank his good friend Mr. John

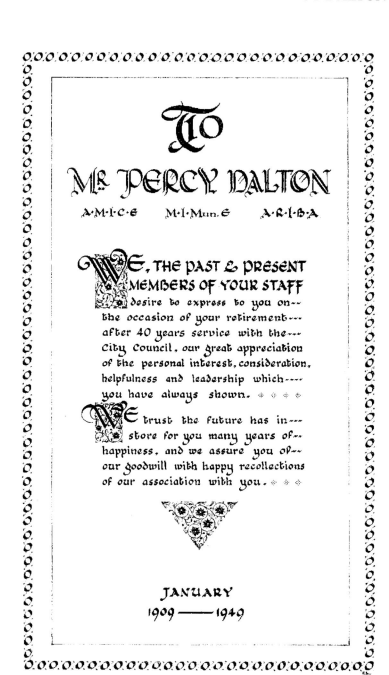

To

Mr PERCY DALTON

A·M·I·C·E   M·I·Mun.E   A·R·I·B·A

WE, THE PAST & PRESENT MEMBERS OF YOUR STAFF desire to express to you on the occasion of your retirement after 40 years service with the City Council, our great appreciation of the personal interest, consideration, helpfulness and leadership which you have always shown. * * *

WE trust the future has in store for you many years of happiness, and we assure you of our goodwill with happy recollections of our association with you. * * *

JANUARY
1909 —— 1949

W. Laing. The following extract is taken from a letter from Mr. Percy Dalton, which was printed in the February 1949 issue of the monthly news sheet, the *Team Spirit*, issued by John Laing & Son Ltd.: "Between the two wars Carlisle at one time or another held various records, so I was informed at the Ministry of Health, Whitehall. This was only possible by your assistance and I shall always feel grateful for your firm's co-operation in carrying out work, which must have contributed so much to the happiness of Carlisle citizens."[16]

After the death of Percy Dalton on 3 May 1957, aged 73, there was an official procession representing the corporation headed by the chief constable of Carlisle and the mayor and mayoress, with the funeral service taking place at Charlotte Street Congregational Church. The minister, the Rev. H. Smith, said: "The man in whose memory they had gathered together to pay there last tributes of esteem and affection had not paraded his qualities and abilities. He had been quiet and modest and one had to be in his company for some time before one noticed his great charm and winsomeness of character and personality.

"His works had been well summed up by the *Cumberland Evening News* with the words: "He changed the face of Carlisle." His works were not the result of sudden and capricious fancy but of stern and determined devotion to duty. In these days when application to work was governed by the clock for many people, the works to which Mr. Dalton's hand was set were never absent from him. He worked too hard; he gave too much to the city he loved so well that when his well-earned retirement came he had not the physical strength to enjoy it. But I am certain that he never begrudged a moment he spent in the pursuit of his work. In the last few years of his life he had been made happy by the knowledge that the fruits of his labours were not in vain."

After the service the cortege proceeded to Stanwix Cemetery where Percy Dalton was interred. Here there is no grand memorial to mark the grave of "the quiet man who changed the face of Carlisle" but a simple modest headstone, perhaps a reflection on the modesty of Mr. Percy Dalton.

J.R. Charnley.
R. Lowthian.
Mr. & Mrs. W. Forsythe
W.I. Bell.
H.W. Rhodes.
G. Creed.
E.A. Tornbohm.
H.M.G. Cockbain.
A.E. Motyer.
W. Johnson.
J. Stewardson.
P. Stewardson.
R. Covill.
J.N. Waite.

W.E. Foster.
J. Dixon.
I.A. Young.
J.L. Campbell.
J. Phillips.
J.D. Blacklock.
G.E. Cooper.
R.D. Robinson.
J.J. Feaver.
John Little.
H.F. Lea.
G. Lindley.
Mrs. W. Burrell.
Mrs. Macdonald.

NOTES

[1] *Life and Belief in the Experience of John W Laing* by Godfrey Harrison.

[2] 17 September 1926, *Carlisle Journal.*)

[3] *Carlisle Journal*

[4] *Carlisle Journal*

[5] Council minutes report

[6] *Carlisle Journal*

[7] 24 October 1926, *Carlisle Journal*

[8] Mannex & Whellan, 1847

[9] Mr. Percy Dalton, October, 1932

[10] Cumbrian Diary, 11 October 1957, *Carlisle Journal*

[11] *Carlisle Journal*, October 1932

[12] *Carlisle Journal*

[13] Memories of old Carlisle, *Carlisle Journal,* 1950

[14] Author's note: The Civic Centre was eventually built in the 1960s and plans for the "great new highway from the west" have been discussed in 2000/2002.

[15] *Carlisle Journal*

[16] See page 98 for signatures of Percy Dalton's staff

MORE BOOKS FROM HAYLOFT

The Herdwick Country Cook Book, Hugh and Therese Southgate
(Hardback, £19.95, 0 9540711 8 2)
(Paperback, £14.95, 0 9540711 7 4)

A History of Kaber, Helen McDonald and Christine Dowson,
(£8.00, ISBN 0 9540711 6 6)

*A Dream Come True, the Life and Times of a Lake District
National Park Ranger,* David Birkett (£5.50, ISBN 0 9540711 5 8)

Gone to Blazes, Life as a Cumbrian Fireman, David Stubbings
(£9.95, ISBN 0 9540711 4 X)

Changing Times, The Millennium Story of Bolton, Barbara Cotton
(£12.50, ISBN 0 9540711 3 1)

*Better by Far a Cumberland Hussar, A History of the Westmorland
and Cumberland Yeomanry,* Colin Bardgett
(Hardback, £26.95, ISBN 0 9540711 2 3)
(Paperback, £16.95, ISBN 0 9540711 1 5)

Northern Warrior, the Story of Sir Andreas de Harcla,
Adrian Rogan
(£8.95, ISBN 0 9523282 8 3)

A Riot of Thorn & Leaf, Dulcie Matthews
(£7.95, ISBN 0 9540711 0 7)

A Country Doctor, Dr. Isaac Bainbridge, Dawn Robertson
(£2.25, ISBN 0 9523282 32)

*Military Mountaineering, A History of Services Expeditions, 1945-
2000,* Retd. SAS Major Bronco Lane
(Hardback, £25.95, ISBN 0 9523282 1 6)
(Paperback, £17.95, ISBN 0 9523282 6 7)

Yows & Cows, A Bit of Westmorland Wit, Mike Sanderson
(£7.95, ISBN 0 9523282 0 8)

Riding the Stang, Dawn Robertson
(£9.99, ISBN 0 9523282 2 4)

Secrets and Legends of Old Westmorland,
Peter Koronka and Dawn Robertson
(Hardback, £17.95, ISBN 0 9523282 4 0)
(Paperback, £11.95, ISBN 0 9523282 9 1)

The Irish Influence, Harold Slight
(£4.95, 0 9523282 5 9)

Soldiers and Sherpas, A Taste for Adventure, Brummie Stokes.
(£19.95, 0 9541551 0 6)

North Country Tapestry, Sylvia Mary McCosh
(£10, 0 9518690 0 0)

Between Two Gardens, The Diary of two Border Gardens,
Sylvia Mary McCosh
(£5.95, 0 9008111 7 X)

Dacre Castle, A short history of the Castle and the Dacre Family,
E. H. A. Stretton
(£5.50, 0 9518690 1 9)

You can order any of our books by writing to:

Hayloft Publishing, Great Skerrygill,
South Stainmore, Kirkby Stephen,
Cumbria, CA17 4EU, UK.

Please enclose a cheque plus £2 for UK postage and packing.
Tel: +44 (0)17683) 42300
For more information see: www.hayloft.org.uk